Aquarium Fish
Dise

Dr. Rolf Geisler

Revised and Expanded Edition

Cover photograph of Cardinal Tetras
by Dr. Herbert R. Axelrod.

Title page:
Obviously healthy *Corydoras paleatus* engaging in pre-spawning maneuvers.*Corydoras* catfish are highly resistant to attacks of Ich, the most common infectious aquarium fish disease. Photo by H.J. Richter.

Distributed in the U.S. by T.F.H. Publications, Inc., 211 West Sylvania Avenue, PO Box 427, Neptune, NJ 07753; in England by T.F.H. (Gt. Britain) Ltd., 13 Nutley Lane, Reigate, Surrey; in Canada to the pet trade by Rolf C. Hagen Ltd., 3225 Sartelon Street, Montreal 382, Quebec; in Canada to the book trade by H & L Pet Supplies, Inc., 27 Kingston Crescent, Kitchener, Ontario N28 2T6; in Southeast Asia by Y.W. Ong, 9 Lorong 36 Geylang, Singapore 14; in Australia and the South Pacific by Pet Imports Pty. Ltd., P.O. Box 149, Brookvale 2100, N.S.W. Australia; in South Africa by Valid Agencies, P.O. Box 51901, Randburg 2125 South Africa. Published by T.F.H. Publications, Inc., Ltd., the British Crown Colony of Hong Kong.

CONTENTS

Healthy tropicals in a healthy environment, the goal of aquarists everywhere. Where proper preventive measures are carried out, there is rarely a need for treatments of any kind.

INTRODUCTION

The German expression "healthy as a fish in water" unfortunately is not always accurate, as fish are frequently very greatly plagued by sickness. All aquarium hobbyists look for pleasure from their pastime, and the professional fish breeder is desirous of success in his work. To attain these ends some knowledge of fish diseases and their cure is essential.

There are some excellent informative works in the wide field of fish diseases, and this booklet is not intended to replace such works. Whoever is acquainted with the problems which constantly crop up in aquarium management knows that the main troubles met with can be traced to relatively few causes. Therefore this booklet may be considered a condensed guide by an aquarist for aquarists, which stresses by experience the *prevention* of fish diseases.

This digital thermometer is attached to the outside glass of the aquarium. These liquid crystal thermometers are highly accurate.

gen. Most aquarium fishes come from tropical waters which even in the winter should never sink below 68° or, better yet, 72°. This holds good for most Characins. Some tropical species like the Discus, Angelfish, Bettas, Pearl Gouramis, and Chocolate Gouramis require water temperatures from 77° to 82° F.

The temperatures given are vitally important to the fishes. Attempts to "toughen" them by giving them occasionally lower temperatures—usually attempts at economy in supplying the required heating—are foolish and will surely lead to trouble. We must remember that in every aquarium there are some parasite carriers. When proper care is given to the fishes these parasites cannot develop to any extent, because fishes then have ample powers of resistance. The moment that these powers are weakened by water which is too cold, the parasites are enabled to multiply and cause damage. For this reason it is of utmost importance to provide a constant and properly regulated water temperature! Drastic changes when moving a fish from tank to tank should be avoided.

The usual results from water temperatures which are too low are skin paleness, fungus, and *Ichthyophonus*.

OXYGEN SCARCITY

Every fish requires a certain amount of oxygen in its water. The normal water capacity of oxygen is dependent upon its temperature. Warmer water has a considerably lower oxygen content than cooler water. Therefore it is possible to run into a scarcity of oxygen in a warm-water aquarium which has a large fish population. Most dangerous time of day comes in the first daylight hours. The oxygen content has dropped to a low point, and the fish are seen to do their emergency breathing: they gulp at the surface of the water.

Vibrator pumps come in many sizes to provide the proper amount of air. Some of these pumps are available with double outlets to supply air to several tanks.

If we do not want our fish to suffocate, speedy help is essential. Aeration alone is seldom enough. Usually the underlying cause is crowded conditions or the presence of uneaten food or feces, giving rise to the mass development of decay bacteria which in turn causes the water to be cloudy and contain suspended matter. Such conditions cause the fish to be particularly sensitive to skin parasites. Therefore cleaning all foreign matter from the bottom, putting in an efficient filter, and giving a partial change of water are just as important as aeration when it comes to eliminating the causes of oxygen shortage.

EXCESSIVE OXYGEN AND GAS BUBBLE DISEASE

If the aquarium contains considerably more oxygen than the normal content calls for, a fish's skin and fins may show plainly visible gas bubbles. These bubbles have the power to clog tiny blood vessels and can cause the fish's death. In the aquarium such a damaging oxygen surplus can take place if there is a dense planting which consists mostly of Anacharis (*Elodea*) and at the same time the aquarium receives a great deal of sunlight. The right thing to do is to guard against overplanting and shield the tank from too much light.

A similar oxygen surplus takes place when an aquarium is filled with water from a tap. The tap water was under pressure in the pipes and at the same time the temperature was low, both leading to a high content of air and oxygen with it. In the aquarium the water becomes de-pressurized and warmed up. The result is a lower capacity for air with its oxygen and consequently the oxygen is formed into tiny bubbles on the glass sides, the plants, and even on the fish. These bubbles can be dangerous for young fry and lead to their death. The remedy is simple: let the tap water stand for 1 or 2 days before using, and at the same time you will also protect against the danger of chlorine.

TOO ACID OR TOO ALKALINE WATER

Fish diseases caused by too acid or too alkaline water only occur if the aquarium water is very soft and deficient in calcium or has had an uncontrolled addition of chemicals. Acid damage is characterized by a milky discoloration of the fish's skin, which can be damaged to a further extent and come off in ragged patches. These symptoms appear at different degrees of acidity with different species. A pH value of less than 5.5 should not be used with aquarium water , even if some fishes (e.g. Discus) can easily withstand pH values as low as 4.5. A measure against this condition is to change the water partially and test for pH value frequently.

DISEASE FROM ALKALIS

This is recognized by a ragged condition of the fins, and at pH values over 9.0 the gills become irritated. In the home aquarium this disease can be expected only when the water contains simple carbonates and is heavily planted with Anacharis, and at the same time the lighting is bright. Under such conditions the plants extract carbon dioxide from the water, and eventually the carbon dioxide combining with the calcium can produce caustic lime. This caustic lime leads to drastic, damaging high pH values. The remedy is a partial change of water, thinning the plants and reducing the light as well as checking with frequent pH measurements.

POISONING

Preventing the outbreak of a disease means avoiding anything which could be damaging to fishes. In this class are the furtive, chronic influxes of poisons. These are frequently traceable to metals which are unprotected from the water. In the aquarium these may be copper and zinc (used in brass heater

Testing the pH of your aquarium water should be part of the regular aquarium maintenance program. Test kits are also available with the necessary chemicals to adjust the pH of your water.

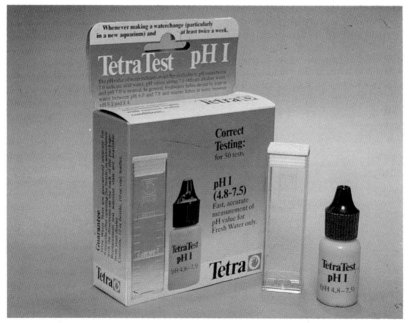

tubes) and more infrequently lead (used for anchoring plants, etc.). The toxic action of these metals is frequently dependent upon the amount of calcium in the water and the pH value.

Metallic copper—frequently used to kill hydra—is particularly poisonous in acid water which is low in calcium. Zinc—perhaps from metal which has been coated with this metal—is very dangerous in the form of zinc chloride, especially if the water contains table salt (resulting in sodium chloride). Salt solution immersions as a cure for skin worm infections must never be given in aquaria with any exposed metal.

Lead, like copper, is dangerous in soft, acid water but does no damage when used in the marine aquarium.

We have not yet heard of any poisoning from iron, such as the rust from the angle-iron frame of an aquarium.

The toxic effects of metals are difficult for the hobbyist to detect. Just the same the poisonous possibilities of metals must be considered, and it is urgently advised to use aquaria with stainless steel frames or to coat other metal surfaces with a reliable coating substance. Aquaria with metal bottoms should have a pane of glass fitted over the bottom and cemented in place.

There are several types of test kits available to keep a constant check on the nitrogen levels in the aquarium water.

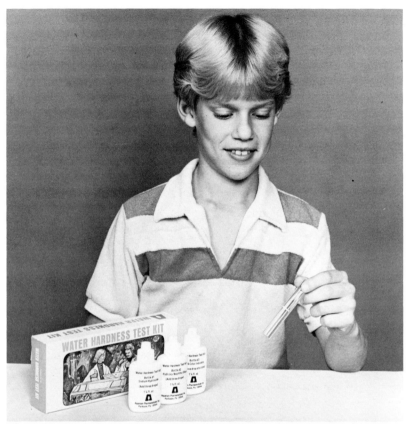

A water hardness kit is an important piece of equipment. Testing water hardness can be done less frequently than testing for changes in the pH level.

Aquarium heaters of metal should be coated or the metal housing replaced with a glass or porcelain tube. There are a number of liquid cements available which may be used on metal parts to give a waterproof, non-toxic coating.

INJURY TO FISHES BY A HIGH NITROGEN CONTENT

As a byproduct of fish life there appears in the water a certain amount of ammonia, which is changed by bacterial action from a nitrite to a nitrate. Although nitrate is nourishment for plant life, the supply in the aquarium is usually much too great to be used up.

14

The best remedy in the freshwater aquarium is a regular partial change of water. In the marine aquarium we must make every effort to save the costly salt water. There are unfortunately very few plants which will grow in the marine aquarium (*Caulerpa* is one), and the result is a rapid rise in nitrogen content, particularly nitrate. Usually a high nitrogen content limits the vitality of fish life. They become droopy, their beautiful colors pale, and they become increasingly prone to parasitic diseases. Partial water changes, in marine aquaria as well as in fresh water, are still the best way to protect against such injury by a too-high nitrogen content.

FISH DISEASE CAUSED BY CHLORINE

Tap water is almost always disinfected with chlorine for the purpose of killing bacteria. Free chlorine and hypochlorous acid usually do deadly work on fish by damaging the gills. Fish poisoned in this manner show very pale gills, with the edges bleached white.

In Europe the chlorine content of tap water is usually about 0.2 mg/l; in the United States greater quantities of chlorine (0.4 mg/l) are usually added. Such a chlorine content is particularly harmful to fry.

It is important for the hobbyist to know that chlorine remains longer in cold water than in warm water before breaking down into harmless constituents. The simplest means to combat chlorine damage is to allow tap water to stand for 48 hours before using in a heated room or with a heater plugged in. If this is not possible, chlorinated water can be made harmless by filtering through activated charcoal. There are also tablets which contain sodium thiosulphate.

NOTE: *For simplicity and ease of application, measurements are listed in metric units.*

> *1 millimeter (mm) = .03937 inch.*
> *1 centimeter (cm) = .3937 inch.*
> *1 gram (g) = 15.432 grains.*
> *1 liter (l) = .9081 quart (dry) or 1.0567 quart (liquid).*
> *1 milligram (mg) = .015432 grain.*
> *1 cubic centimeter (c c) = 1/1000 liter.*

NUTRITIONAL DAMAGE

We must constantly repeat that the prevention of fish illnesses is highly important to the fish hobbyist. A biologically correct nourishment of fish plays a very important part in this. Unfortunately, poor health caused by incorrect nutrition is also widespread among aquarium fishes. A good 90% of all aquarium fishes are fed with dry foods and *Tubifex* worms. The pains taken by manufacturers to provide a constantly better grade of dry food, perhaps by the addition of vitamins, are very praiseworthy, but most fish breeders know that success in fish-keeping requires above all a varied feeding with living foods.

FATTENING

The most important nutritional damage is fattening, caused by a too generous feeding with dry foods, white worms and Grindal worms, coupled with a lack of activity in small aquaria. This leads to fattening of the internal organs, especially of the most important one, the liver, which causes a severe upset in the metabolism of the fish. The reproductive organs, particularly the ovaries, are seriously affected. Eggs which are clear in healthy fish are

Freeze-dried foods are available in several varieties. Shown here are freeze-dried brine shrimp and tubifex worms. A varied diet is essential to the health of the fishes.

1. A variety of fish foods including freeze-dried foods, pellets, flakes, and tablets. 2. Brine shrimp flakes. 3. A color-enhancing flake food with added vitamins.

clouded milky-white in fattened females, causing faulty development or a complete lack of it. Egg binding in females, which we hear about so often, is a result of faulty feeding and care. One leading authority on fish diseases, Dr. Schäperclaus, says as a result of his long experience:

"There is scarcely a single aquarium fish which has been kept for several years in captivity that does not show a greater or lesser form of fattening. Again and again I concluded from post-mortem examinations that fattening of the organs is the most frequent cause of death in fishes which had been kept in captivity for a year or more. The conclusion that these metabolic illnesses and disturbances are to no small extent the cause of devastating spread of most parasites should be an incentive to do everything in one's power to prevent such fattening, because a subsequent cure is scarcely possible."

INTESTINAL INFLAMMATION

This disease occurs readily when there is a one-sided poor feeding or a too greatly concentrated diet of foods that have a high salt content, or by feeding too heavily with blood larvae and white worms. In a period of a few hours the entire population of a tank can be affected. When the fish are opened the intestines and anus are deeply reddened and usually erupted in heavy blisters.

The blood larvae and *Tubifex* worms available for purchase all come from waters which are mixed with much organic wastes. Such waters, which are scarcely or not at all habitable to fish life, are tremendously rich in decay bacteria. Before we feed blood larvae or *Tubifex* worms, we must for this reason cleanse them of all sewage and mud particles, preferably by keeping them in *running* water. Afterwards we must be sure to feed only small portions. Blood larvae are difficult for small fishes to digest, and frequently they are passed by the fish practically undigested. Therefore be careful!

EGG BINDING

Normally every fish in its natural waters finds it possible to spawn during its normal period of ripeness. In the aquarium this is frequently not the case, and the eggs must be dissolved and resorbed by the fish's body. When a fish has been poorly nourished and poorly kept (too little space, too low temperature, etc.) this resorbtion is made difficult and the fattened eggs usually become hard. Such fish are no longer capable of breeding, and the upsets in metabolism caused by the hardening of the eggs are so profound that females so affected are doomed to die.

Attempts to strip off the hardened eggs artificially are only seldom successful, and usually the only result is damage to the internal organs. The correct way, therefore, is to prevent egg binding and especially nutritional defects by following these rules:

Feed a varied diet of live foods (*Daphnia, Cyclops,* blood larvae, glass larvae, mosquito larvae) as well as lettuce and algae. *Tubifex* and white worms are not complete substitutes for other live foods. Feed small portions several times a day. Small portions of good foods, fed frequently, are better than larger portions only once a day.

Give your fish plenty of space and the proper temperature.

The upper fish, the female of this pair of Zebra Danios, is heavily distended with roe. Egg-binding is not too uncommon in aquarium fishes, especially those which have been fed on a diet of fattening foods. Photo by G.J.M. Timmerman.

FISH DISEASES CAUSED BY EXTERNAL PARASITES

External parasites are those which confine their activities to the outside of a fish or burrow into its skin. Such parasites are much easier to overcome than the internal ones by the use of immersions, which will be explained later.

ICHTHYOPHTHIRIUS

This parasite, which occurs all over the world and mostly in fresh water, can also crop up in brackish and marine water. It belongs to the scientific group of single-celled animals, the Protozoa, in the class Ciliata. *Ichthyophthirius* is parasitic for part of its life in the fish's skin. Grown specimens there attain a size of 1 mm, large for a one-celled animal. A fish with a severe attack looks as if it were sprinkled with cereal. When such spots become visible on the body or fins, the fish is suffering from the dangerous "Ich," as many aquarists have come to call it. As a heavy attack can cause death in an aquarium

A hatchet fish with ich. Raised blisters about the size of a grain of salt are present on the fins and body. Illustration © 1979 by Wardley Products Co.

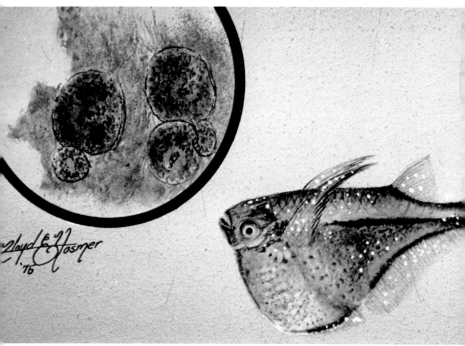

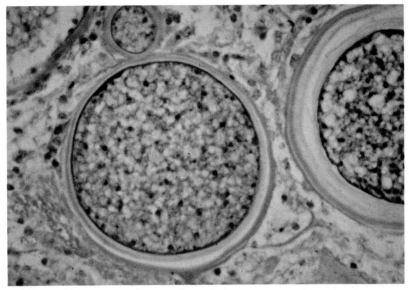

Highly magnified *Ichthyopthirius* spores in the liver of a yellowtail flounder. Photo courtesy of George D. Ruggieri and R.F. Nigrelli.

Photomicrograph of ich parasites imbedded in the skin. Courtesy of Dr. Sylvan Cohen.

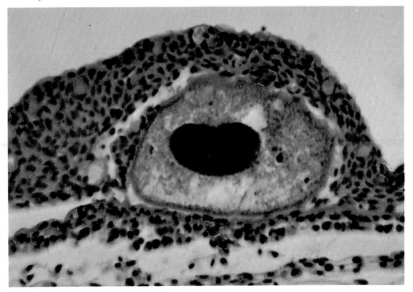

fish—with sensitive young fry it takes only 2 or 3 parasites—it is very important to be able to recognize such an infection in its early stages.

Ich shows developmental stages which must be known in order to combat it effectively and with the utmost safety to the affected fish. In the first stages of development Ich is very small (about 5/1000 mm) and can therefore be seen only with a microscope. These little "swarmers" which have a pearlike shape bore into the fish's skin, especially between the outer skin and the subcutaneous layer. Here in the skin the parasites feed on their fish host, growing to a size of 1 mm or more. What we then see with the naked eye as little white spots are the parasites in their growing and mature stages. Mature parasites then leave their host through a hole in the skin and then become free-swimming parasites, later becoming encysted. Inside of this cyst the mother parasite separates herself into many—up to 1000—daughter parasites. These then leave the cyst and try as free-swimming creatures to find another fish into whose body they can bore and in whose skin they can lead a parasitic existence.

A highly magnified view of the Ich parasite itself. Photo by Helmert.

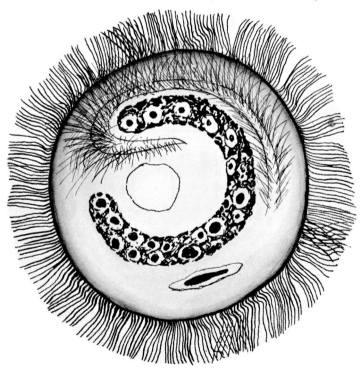

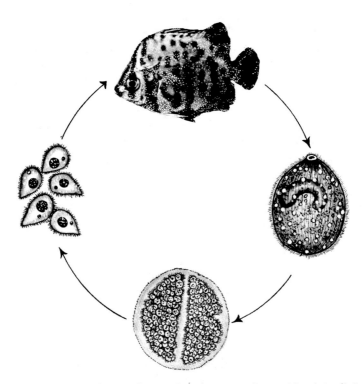

The Ich cycle, from fish to free-swimming parasite and back to fish.

This developmental stage makes it plain that Ich can multiply tremendously by the formation of daughter parasites, the swarming creatures. The effect in crowded aquaria is widespread death. The battle against "white-spot," as our British friends call it, must therefore be *immediately* begun as soon as the first white spots are discovered. Any delay can be costly, because a heavy infestation of Ich can damage a fish's skin so badly that it will die.

The destruction of Ich is possible only in the "swarming" stage, the stage which is invisible to the naked eye. White spots which are visible on the fish are the cysts which have already imbedded themselves in the fish's skin, and while in this state they cannot be destroyed. We must therefore concentrate our efforts against the stages which are found in the water.

A conquest without the use of chemicals is the "change-over method." We know that the "swarmers" in a certain temperature range must find a host within about 50 hours, and will starve to death if they do not find a host within this time. Therefore we can destroy Ich by changing the fish every 12 hours into a tank of clean, parasite-free water. Because the parasites in a clean tank without fish life are dead after 3 days, we require 7 tanks for this cure. This is somewhat inconvenient, but this method has a great advantage over the use of chemicals. Plants are not damaged, as they easily might be otherwise.

Destroying Ich by means of chemical baths should not therefore be carried out in planted aquaria but in isolated containers such as, for instance, an unused all-glass aquarium. The aquarium may be used again after the treatments, because all the parasistes die in 3 days when left in an empty tank. The petshops offer a number of preparations which are effective when used exactly as directed. An old favorite is a bath in an acriflavine solution (1 g to 100 liters of water) or the use of quinine salts (1 g of quinine hydrochloride or quinine sulphate to 100 liters of water). The claim that fish become sterile after being treated with quinine has never been proven. In particularly stubborn cases of Ich a combination of acriflavine and methylene blue (1 g each to 100-150 liters of water) has proven effective.

Xenomystus nigri suffering from white spot disease, caused by *Ichthyophthirius multifiliis.* Photo by Frickhinger.

A diatomaceous earth filter will filter out many protozoan parasites such as ich. These filters will change murky water to sparkling-clear water in a matter of minutes.

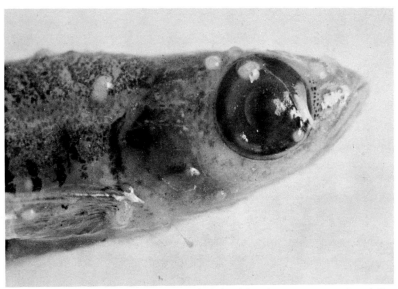

The white nodules shown on the fish in this closeup are cysts of the parasite *Ichthyophthirius.* Photo by Helmert.

A smear of the skin of a fish infected by Ich. Photo by Helmert.

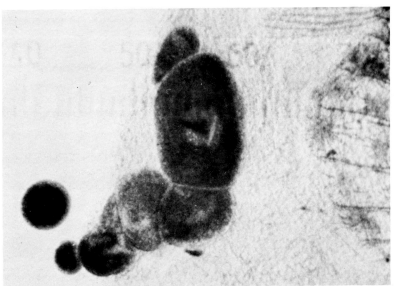

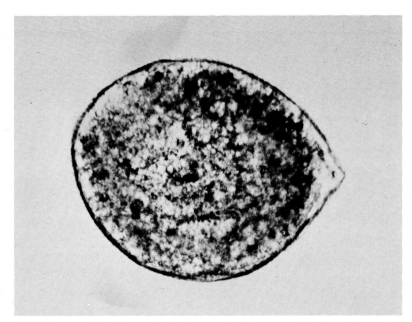

A highly magnified view of a freely moving Ich spore. Photo by Helmert.

The fish must be kept in the solutions referred to until all the parasites have left the skin. The time required at a temperature of 74° to 77°, allowing for an added period of safety, is 9 or 10 days.

If it is necessary to use a set-up tank for the treatment, the water should be replaced with fresh water afterwards. Ich can be avoided by a quarantine period of at least a week. Live foods from a pond which has a fish population should stand for 3 to 4 days before being fed, in order to kill or organisms which may exist. Ich can be transported on aquatic plants, so precautions are also recommended here.

VELVET DISEASE

The causes of the contagious "velvet" disease are also one-celled organisms, of the genera *Costia*, *Cyclochaete* and *Chilodonella*. These microscopically tiny parasites—their size is about 3/200 mm—feed on the skin and gills. Fish which have fallen prey often scrape against the bottom or stones. A heavier infection results in folded fins, with the fish becoming tired and weak. Often the skin shows an indistinct bluish-white covering, caused by a mass development of the previously-named parasites.

As it is only rarely possible for the hobbyist to identify by a microscopic examination the presence of *Costia* and similar organisms, there are preventive measures when the other symptoms appear, such as scratching and folded fins, because velvet is one of the most common of fish diseases, especially in crowded aquaria, in raising tanks, and with fish that have been weakened by traveling, where losses can be high. Poorly nourished fish, and those that have been kept under poor conditions (like too-low temperatures) are ready victims of velvet disease. Where this is concerned, it is not always necessary

Ultraviolet steriliz-ing units are used to kill bacteria in aquarium water. These filters can be used on freshwater or marine aquar-iums.

Female *Nothobranchius korthause* infected with *Oodinium* (velvet) parasite. Photo by H. J. Richter.

to bring it in freshly. Even healthy fish always have some organisms, which do no amount of harm until they multiply in great numbers when the fish's resistive powers are low. It is therefore not enough to fight velvet outbreaks only with immersions, because the fish must be kept under optimum conditions at this time.

When the outbreak is a light one, it is merely necessary to raise the temperature to 82°-86° for 2 to 3 days (don't forget the aeration!). For heavier infestations, baths in an acriflavine solution (2 to 3 days, 1 g to 100 liters of water). As acriflavine can be harmful to aquatic plants, the use of a spare tank for the solution is safest, and at the same time the chemical concentration can change quickly and uncontrollably in a set-up aquarium.

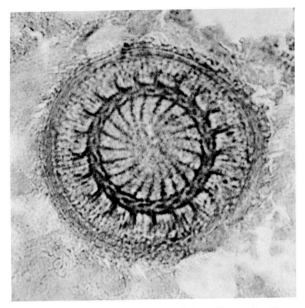

Cyclochaete domerguei, from a smear of the slime of a diseased fish.
Photo by C. van Duijn, Jr.

Chilodonella parasites, greatly enlarged. Photo by Helmert.

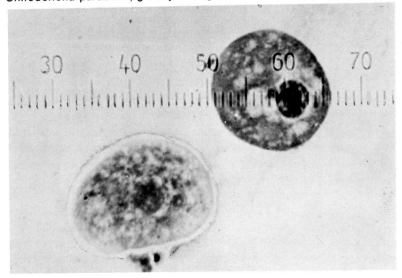

FIN ROT

Aquarium hobbyists often speak of "fin rot." This term is used to cover a multitude of diseases with various causes such as infections with aquatic bacteria and with the causers of "velvet," the aftermath of *Ichthyophonus* or hereditary traits.

With bacterial fin rot the fin edges are first attacked, followed afterwards by a spread of the inflammations and the fins coming loose in little ragged bits.

A magnified view of a tumor in the tail of a fish resulting from a Platy-Swordtail cross. The photo shows the pigments and an accumulation of giant cells. Photo by Dr. Rolf Geisler.

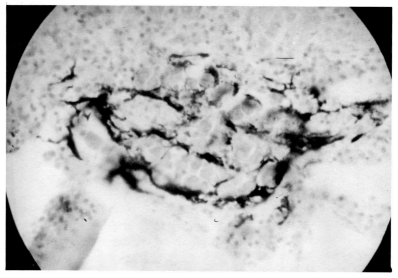

Often afterwards there is a secondary infection by the fungus *Saprolegnia.* Fishes with a heavy case of fin rot have been frequently considered as candidates for death, because immersions in chemical solutions have only seldom been successful in healing the disease in its advanced stages. Following the great success in dealing with human bacterial ailments by the use of antibiotics, it was found that aquatic bacteria could be successfully dealt with in the same manner, as was done with so-called "carp dropsy" in the commercial breeding of this food fish. In Europe, such antibiotics as penicillin or aureomycin can be obtained by prescription only and for this reason are still little used by aquarium hobbyists. On the other hand, in the United States aureomycin is used to deal with fin rot, even in a dosage of 250 to 500 mg to every 5 liters of water.

Hereditary fin rot is well-known with various breeds, such as hybrids between Swordtails (*Xiphophorus helleri*) and the closely-related Platies (*Xiphophorus maculatus*). Especially with the all-black and the black and red breeds one often finds genetically-originated fin defects and fin damage, against which we can do nothing but to give them the best of conditions.

A spotted headstander suffering from fin and tail rot. Illustration © 1979 Wardley Products Co.

The white patches on this goldfish are areas infected by the fungus *Saprolegnia*. A fish in good health is usually not susceptible to *Saprolegnia* infection; only injured and bruised parts of the body are attacked.

OODINIUM IN MARINE FISHES

Parasitic algae of the genus *Oodinium* are the source of skin and gill diseases in fresh and marine water. While the infection seldom causes severe damage among fresh-water fishes, *Oodinium* can lead to the worst outbreaks among the marine species.

The opaque, oval, dark parasites of 3/10 to 1/10 mm in diameter can be recognized plainly only under a microscope and have developmental stages which are very similar to *Ichthyophthirius*. After the parasitic stage on the skin and gills, *Oodinium* breaks loose and in warm water divides into 256 free-swimming organisms in the course of approximately 2 days. These in turn try to find another fish. *Oodinium* is therefore capable of multiplying with extraordinary rapidity and is the most dangerous disease to attack marine aquarium fishes. With fresh-water aquarium fishes *Oodinium* can be cured with a sustained immersion in an acriflavine solution such as we have already described for *Ichthyophthirius*. It is also beneficial to darken the aquarium considerably. Because it would be damaging to the plants to be deprived of their light, it is again advisable to undertake the treatment in a separate aquarium..

With marine fishes the cure of *Oodinium* by treatment with copper sulphate as proposed by Dempster has proven to be of value. Copper solutions are known to be highly poisonous to aquatic organisms. Copper in the form of copper sulphate must for this reason be added in exact dosages in order to kill the parasite without harming the fish. The concentration according to Dempster should not exceed 0.8 mg per liter, and for sensitive fishes 0.4 mg per liter. Because of the varying toxicity of copper on different species it is advisable to begin with a solution of not more than 0.5 mg per liter.

This is how the procedure goes: First, the exact water content of the aquarium must be computed in liters (length $\times$ breadth $\times$ height of the water, in metric measures). Have a pharmacist make up a solution of 3.93 of "analytical copper sulphate" (the specific chemical formula is $CuSO_4 \cdot 5H_2O$) in 1 liter of distilled water. One cc of this solution will then contain 3.93 mg of copper sulphate, corresponding to 1 mg per liter of copper. For every liter of salt water we will require 0.5 cc of this solution for combating the disease; for example, an aquarium containing 80 liters of water would get 80×0.5, or 40 cc of the solution. The exact measure of the solution is made by means of a pipette, which can be purchased in any store that sells laboratory equipment.

It has already been indicated that copper in hard and weakly alkaline water dissolves less readily than copper in calcium-poor, acid water. These stipulations are given to show how during the 10-day immersion against "marine fish disease" a part of the copper is separated in insoluble form. Because of this the copper concentration becomes weaker, as does the effectiveness against *Oodinium*. Therefore some copper sulphate solution must be added. This is not so simple if the possibility does not exist in exceptional cases to check the water chemically. Some marine fish hobbyists add traces of copper even when the fish are not acutely sick, by adding a piece of sheet copper to the aquarium.

FUNGUS

Every place where fishes are injured by true parasites such as velvet or Ich or are damaged by careless netting, or by the bites of their tankmates or by banging against solid objects in tanks which are too small for them, we will find wounds on the mouth, body, or fins. These wounds are easily attacked by "fungus." This term encompasses the ubiquitous aquatic fungi of the genera *Saprolegnia* and *Achyla*, which attack not only living fishes but also damaged fish eggs and uneaten food. In contrast to the parasites already mentioned, an attack by *Saprolegnia* on a fish is always a consequence to previous

Saprolegnia infection in the skin of a fish.

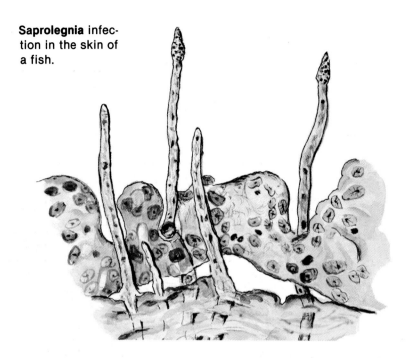

Cross-section of the thread-like formation of the fungus *Saprolegnia*. Photo by Helmert.

damage, with *Saprolegnia* as a secondary occurrence. For this reason it is important to prevent any injuries to fish, which can partly be summed up thus:

Do not use too coarse netting (skin injuries!).

Give your fish plenty of room (or there will be mouth fungus, especially among livebearers).

An angelfish with mouth fungus. With proper medication mouth fungus can be controlled. Illustration © 1979 Wardley Products Co.

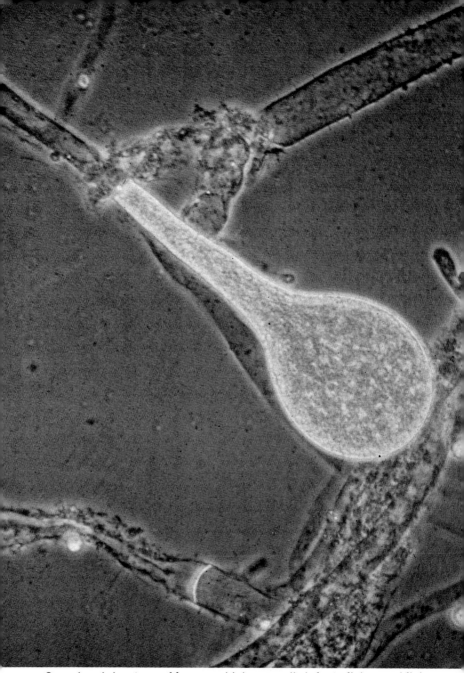

Saprolegnia is a type of fungus which generally infects fishes and fish eggs. The eggs of mouth-brooders are specially susceptible to fungus attacks. Photo by Dr. H. Reichenbach-Klinke.

Avoid using sharp-edged rocks or sharp-edged gravel in the aquarium.

Skin parasites like velvet and Ich should be treated as soon as they are recognized.

It is also important to rid the tank of all decaying matter and uneaten food, thereby depriving the fungi of any possibility to thrive.

Such fishes as have been heavily attacked with a cottony grayish-white fungus are very difficult to heal; if they are small, the job is almost impossible. Protection from fungus is therefore important. If the damage is done, small outbreaks of fungus on such places as the mouth usually heal themselves in a clean aquarium with sufficient heat, good filtration and a proper amount of oxygen. Chemical baths with a thorough action are scarcely known. The suggested treatment is with potassium permanganate. Larger patches are swabbed with a solution of 1 g potassium permanganate to the liter of water, applied with a swab made by twisting a bit of cotton on the end of a wooden tooth-pick. Then the fish are returned to a solution of 1 g to 100 liters of water (8-10 hours at most for larger fishes, small ones $1\frac{1}{2}$-2 hours). After this the fish must be given the best possible surroundings for recovery.

A familiar sight to every fish breeder is the attack by fungus of infertile, damaged, or dead fish eggs. Because the fungus can be carried from an affected egg to a healthy one alongside, fungused eggs must be removed at once. Frequently acriflavine is added to the water to prevent fungus infection, but this is not very effective. A new preventive against *Saprolegnia* has been found in recent years by working with trout and other food fishes. This is a dye, malachite green. Findings where aquarium fishes are concerned have not yet been published, but a basis for experiments with malachite green immersions would be a concentration of 0.2 g to 100 liters of water. Duration of immersions should be as short as possible, and in every case the fish should be carefully observed during the immersion.

INTERNAL PARASITES

Unfortunately, fish are prone to attacks by a great many different internal parasites, under which we can class worms and unicellulars like spore animalcules, flagellates, ciliates, and (more remotely) fungi and bacteria. The limited space to which this little guide is confined can deal with only the most important internal parasites. In general it must be said that it is very difficult to combat internal fish parasites effectively. For this reason disease prevention, that is, preventing their introduction and spread, is of the greatest importance.

ICHTHYOPHONUS

The greatest scourge of all aquarium fishes is without doubt an outbreak of the fungus *Ichthyophonus* (lately classified as *Ichthyosporidium*). According to the findings of world-renowned specialists, from 50% to 60% of all fish deaths in the aquarium are traceable to this. *Ichthyophonus*, to call it by the name which it has long carried, lives in the tissues of the attacked fish and can become parasitic practically anywhere: in the kidneys, liver, reproductive organs, muscles, skin, eyes, fins, gills, and more rarely in the brain as well. Because of the numerous organs which can be affected, the picture presented

Ichthyophonus infection in a Black Molly. Photo by Dr. Rolf Geisler.

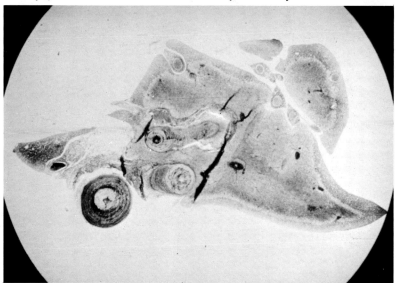

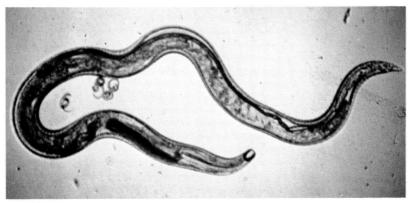

Philometra, a nematode which gives live birth to its young. Notice the five young being born. Photo by Frickhinger.

Philometra (Thwaitia) abdominalis, the blood worm, lives under the gill cover or in the body cavity of fish. The intermediate host of this worm is a copepod.

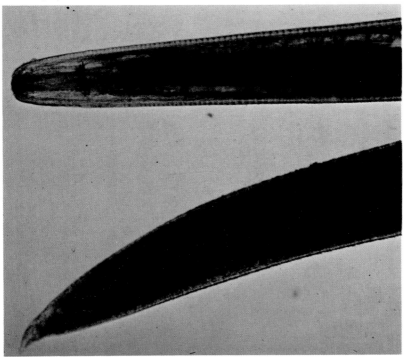

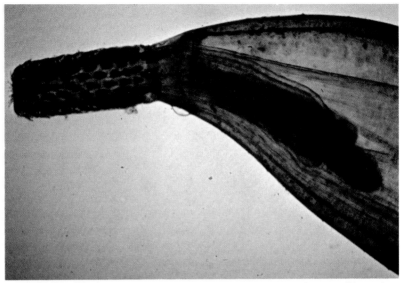

Echinorhynchus taken from body of *Ctenopoma acutirostre*. Photo by Dr. H.-H. Reichenbach.

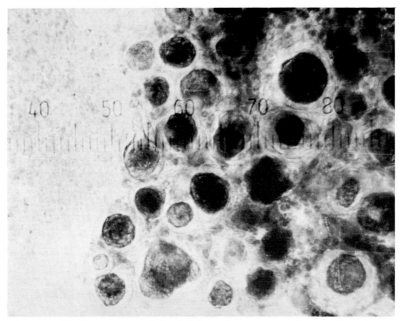

Above and below: cysts of the **Ichthyophonus** parasite greatly enlarged. A millimeter scale has been superimposed for comparison of sizes.

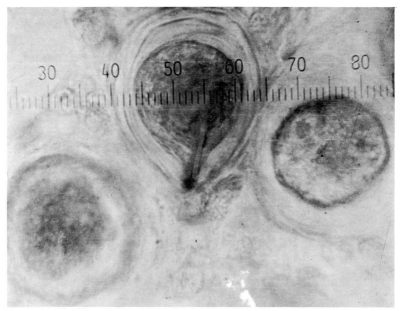

This Betta's fins show the effects of an infection by *Ichthyophonus*. Photo by Helmert.

In this Kribensis the primary area of infection has centered in the skin, as evidenced by the white patches on the body. Photo by Helmert.

can be quite varied. A sure diagnosis requires the use of a microscope, which will show globular blackish-brown fungi up to 3/10 mm in diameter.

There are, however, a number of symptoms which can be attributed to *Ichthyophonus:* loss of fins or ragged fins, tumors, lumps or lesions of the skin, frequently on the head, pop-eyes and eyes falling out, emaciation in spite of good feeding, dark or black body color, or constant gasping at the surface in spite of a good oxygen supply. All fish deaths which show no external symptoms at any time can be suspected to have been caused by

A clean aquarium environment is essential to maintaining healthy fishes. There are many accessories to assist the hobbyist in cleaning the aquarium.

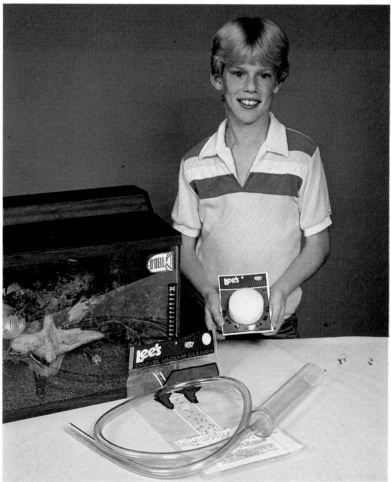

Ichthyophonus. This fungus can spread itself very quickly in the aquarium by being released from open lesions of the skin, by feces which has passed through infected intestines, or by being spread from diseased gills; all these are means of releasing parasites into the open water, where they can again be picked up by other fish while eating. The fungus is also frequently spread by diseased food fishes, as has been proven in many cases.

The successful cure of *Ichthyophonus* by medication is not yet possible. There have been many experiments made by specialists in fish diseases with the purpose of finding a proper medication, such as has been used in the cure of other fungus diseases in humans. However, with some fishes, with even the most careful procedures, the fungi can become encapsulated in the tissues

Plasmodiums of *Ichthyosporidium hoferi* emerging from a cyst in the liver of a rainbow trout.

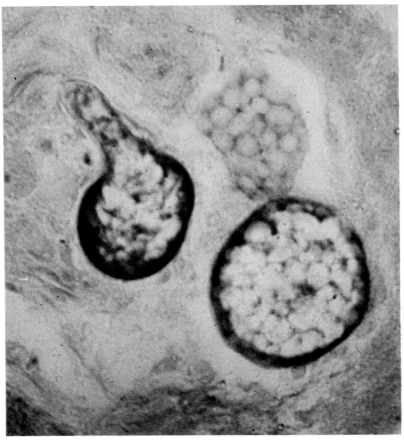

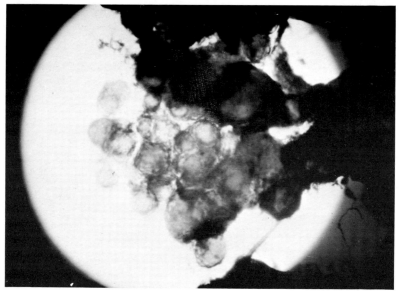

Ichthyophonus infection in a Neon Tetra. Photo by Dr. Rolf Geisler.

Ichthyophonus infection in *Hyphessobrycon ornatus.* Photo by Dr. Rolf Geisler.

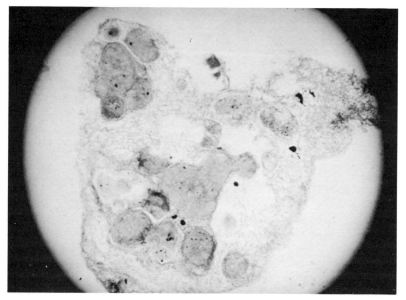

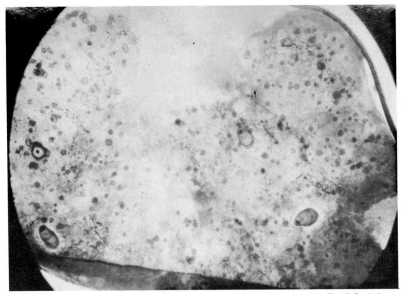
Ichthyophonus infection in Betta splendens. Photo by Dr. Rolf Geisler.

and the disease can be brought to a standstill. Such fish can appear healthy externally, but poor conditions can cause the disease to break out anew and infect other healthy fish. For this reason *Ichthyophonus* is a stealthy and highly dangerous disease of aquarium fishes, in both fresh and salt water.

In order to overcome this disease, fish which have a severe outbreak must be unfailingly destroyed, and then the aquarium must be thoroughly disinfected. If, however, only a few fish are affected, these should be segregated and killed and the rest given exceptionally good treatment until the disease is at a standstill. It is hoped that scientists will soon find a cure for *Ichthyophonus*.

PLISTOPHORA INFECTION (NEON DISEASE)

Especially with the Neon Tetra (*Paracheirodon*, formerly *Hyphessobrycon*, *innesi*) one frequently encounters a considerable paleness of the red color and light to white patches in the region of the tail and back, until finally the red stripe disappears altogether. The cause of this internal disease, which mainly attacks Neon Tetras but could also appear in the Glowlight Tetra and closely related species, is an infection by a parasitic unicellular organism, a spore animalcule of the genus *Plistophora*. When one observes the finely torn-up tissues of such whitish bits of muscle tissue under the microscope, one sees

47

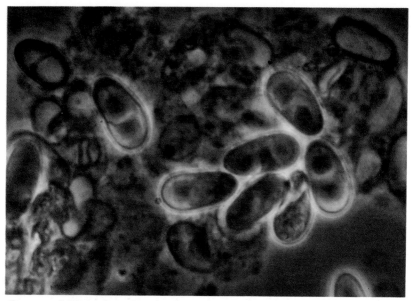

Spores of *Plistophora ovariae* from the ovaries of golden shiner. Photo by Dr. R. Summerfelt.

A neon tetra showing signs of *Plistophora* infection. Photo by S. Frank.

among the muscle fibers globular structures about 3/100 mm in diameter, which are filled with very tiny daughter spores which are 1/200 mm in diameter. The daughter spores are released when the mother structure bursts. In this manner a constant self-infection takes place. The transfer from fish to fish is brought about by spores which have dropped from the damaged muscular tissue and are then picked up by another fish. For the breeder it is of the utmost importance that the ovaries of the fish could be overridden with *Plistophora* and in this manner the disease could be transferred through the eggs. "Neon Disease," which evidently occurs in the fish's natural waters and is not infrequently observed in imported specimens, can seriously hamper the breeding of this lovely fish, and losses among fry are often very heavy. There is no known medication.

The only way that *Plistophora* can be controlled is by killing affected fish and then thoroughly disinfecting the aquarium. Experience has shown that the proper conditions do not prevent an infection, but can bring it to a stand-still. The infected sections of muscle are then encapsulated and the fish can stay alive for quite a time. Success is largely a matter of water characteristics. If we give the fish conditions which resemble those of their home waters, namely very soft, almost calcium-free water with a distinctly acid reaction (pH value between 5.0 and 6.0) which has been created by peat moss filtration,

Plistophora taken from the body of a Neon Tetra. The parasite here is shown in the pansporoblast stage. Photo by Frickhinger.

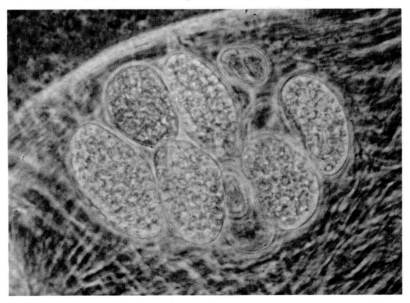

Plistophora infections are accompanied by an almost complete washing-out of the body color, as shown here. Infected fishes in advanced stages of the disease often show a curvature of the spine. Photo by Helmert.

Here the *Plistophora* organisms are shown encased within the muscle fibers of a fish which they have attacked. Photo by Helmert.

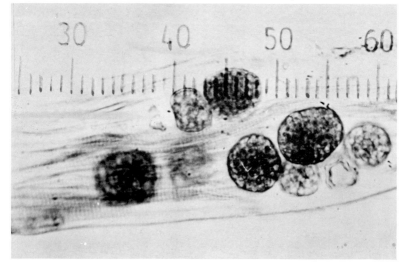

a *Plistophora* infection does not stand anywhere as much chance to get a foothold as strongly as it would in hard, alkaline water. It is also important that the Neons do not come in contact with any spores which have fallen to the bottom. Some expert hobbyists suggest that a thin layer of peat moss be spread over the bottom. Any spores which fall into this are kept away from the fish. The peat moss can be siphoned out with a hose and made free of spores for re-use by boiling.

FISH TUBERCULOSIS

The opinions of scientists about the meaning of fish tuberculosis are not unanimous. The only thing that is known positively is that there are also bacteria among fishes which have a great resemblance to human tuberculosis. However, these mycobacteria exist at an optimum temperature of 103° F., while the bacteria of fish tuberculosis multiply best at 64 to 77° F. In this

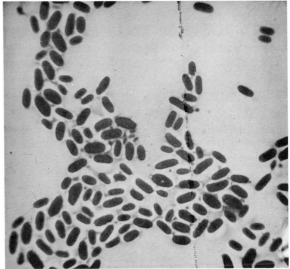

Bacterium lepidorthosae, from a pure culture. Photo by C. van Duijn, Jr.

connection it may be remarked that there would be no danger of infection to humans from tubercular fishes, and that there is no fish disease whatsoever among aquarium fishes which can be transferred to humans.

The tuberculosis germs form tiny lumps or tubercles in the fish. The organs which are attacked are varied. As our knowledge of the bacteria involved is possible only with special examinations and there have been no usable chemical cures, it remains for the hobbyist and breeder to keep his fish under the best conditions and separate any fish suspected of disease.

DROPSY AND SCALE PROTRUSION

These infections, whose name describes the symptoms, are caused by bacteria of the genus *Pseudomonas*. Dropsy has been treated with great success in food fishes by injections of antibiotics. With the comparatively small aquarium fishes this treatment is hardly or not at all possible (with the possible exception of some of the larger Cichlids, such as *Symphysodon* or *Pterophyllum*). The fish must therefore be given immersions in antibiotics, as has been described in the section dealing with fin rot.

This is how a severe pop-eye infection looks when viewed from above. The affected fish shown is a Swordtail, *Xiphophorus helleri*. Photo by Frickhinger.

A dropsical fish (a barb) as viewed from above. The scales have begun to stand out at angles from the body. Photo by Frickhinger.

POP-EYES

One of the most frequently observed diseases is a protrusion of the eye-sockets, the formation of "pop-eyes." Such a disease can have a number of causes. Usually this is the after-effect of an infection by *Ichthyophonus* or *Pseudomonas* bacteria. In some cases of pop-eyes one can easily observe the distinct formation of a gas bubble in the eye, caused by gas-forming bacteria. There is no known cure for this type of pop-eye infection. When the condition is caused by *Ichthyophonus*, the fish should be killed painlessly. Gas-forming bacteria often cause the entire lens of the eye to come out, and such wounds often heal very well unexpectedly, even if the fish has lost the sight of the affected eye.

WORM DISEASES

Skin, gill and intestinal worms are found among fishes in great variety, and only the skin and gill worms can be dealt with directly. The well-known *Gyrodactylus* can be seen with the naked eye, but can be observed more closely with the aid of a magnifying glass. It can best be eliminated by a brief immersion in a salt solution (10 g table salt to 1 liter of water, lasting 20 minutes). Intestinal worms can only be prevented when there is the knowledge that many worms are carried into the aquarium by other creatures, the so-called "intermediate hosts." These should be known to the aquarist, so that he can eliminate the danger of introducing the worms into his aquarium.

The snail *Lymnaea stagnalis* is capable of carrying a worm cataract to fishes, when the snails come from open waters. So be careful!

Blood larvae are intermediate hosts for threadworms, but it is not precisely known to what extent these threadworms are dangerous to fish. As blood larvae from some places are heavily infested with worms—the white, threadlike worms can often be seen crawling right out of the larvae—we advise that such larvae should not be fed to the fish. *Gammarus* are an excellent fish food if they come from waters which are free of fish life. In waters with a fish population one often sees *Gammarus* with a distinct red spot in the brown body. This red spot is the intermediate stage of a sucking worm which lodges in the intestines of a fish as its final host. It is therefore important to separate and destroy such red-spotted *Gammarus* before feeding.

The scratcher worm, *Echinorhynchus nodulosus*. Photo by Dr. J. Knaack.

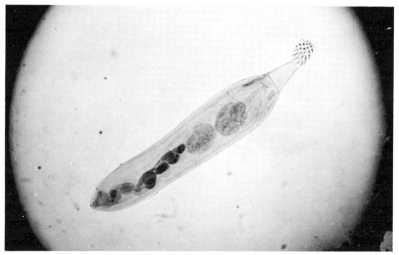

An intestinal worm parasite, *Dicrocoelium lanceolatum*. Photo by Dr. J. Knaack.

Diplozoon paradoxum, a worm which attacks the gills. Photo by Dr. J. Knaack.

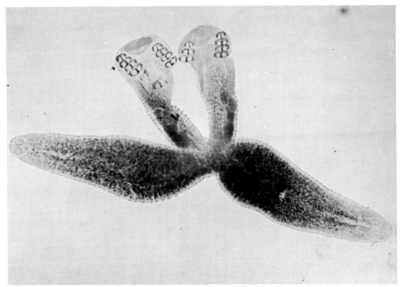

DISINFECTING THE AQUARIUM

It has been frequently asked if it is necessary to disinfect an aquarium after a parasitic fish disease. We cannot give an answer which covers all cases. If the external parasites here described were responsible for the disease, the treatment of the fish has either completely destroyed the parasites or reduced their numbers so greatly that a special disinfection of the aquarium is no longer necessary.

However, where there was an attack of the very dangerous internal parasites *Ichthyophonus* or *Plistophora* it is very easily possible that healthy fishes could become sick if the aquarium is not thoroughly disinfected. To do this the aquarium must first be cleared and the plants—much as this may hurt —be thrown out. It is also best to remove the bottom gravel and replace it. The aquarium which is now empty is filled to the brim with fresh water and the disinfecting medium added. Potassium permanganate is good for the purpose, being inexpensive and easily obtainable everywhere. Use 1 g to every 10 liters of water, allowing the deep red to violet mixture to remain there for 4 to 5 days and stirring frequently. Fresh water can then be added. If there is a brown deposit on the glass or bottom, it can be removed with a dilute solution of sodium bisulfite.

A very strong disinfection can be attained with chlorine preparations. Because chlorine is very poisonous, it must be used with great care, using something like a dilute solution of chlorine bleach (sodium hypochloride). Chloramine tablets are harmless and may be purchased in any pharmacy and used according to instructions (2% solution). It is self-evident—but often forgotten—that fish nets must also be disinfected, or disinfecting everything else will be useless.

REVIEW AND TREATMENT OF THE IMPORTANT FISH DISEASES

Organ and Symptoms	Usual Cause	Treatment
Skin and fins		
Bluish-white discoloration	Velvet disease	Chemical immersions, 20
Same, usually with marine fishes	*Oodinium*	Chemical immersions, 22
Skin discolorations, ragged fins	Acidity	Neutralization of water, 8
Cottony, grayish-white fungus formations	*Saprolegnia*	Immersions, improvement of conditions, 26, 25
Grainy white spots (up to 1 mm in size)	*Ichthyophthirius*	Chemical immersions, 16
Same, usually with marine fishes	*Oodinium*	Copper immersions, 22
Sores on and in the skin, holes, fin disorders	*Ichthyophonus* bacterial infection	
Gills		
Spread-out gill plates	Velvet, parasitic worms, lack of oxygen	Chemical immersions, 20, 38
	Mass development of decay bacteria	Water filtration
Same, usually with marine fishes	*Oodinium*	Copper immersions, 22
Muscles		
"Holes" especially in the head of Discus	*Ichthyophonus*	
Whitish transparent areas or whitish lumps, especially with Neons	*Plistophora* (Neon disease)	
Eyes		
Protrusion	Bacteria	Acriflavine immersion
	Gas-bubble disease	
	Ichthyophonus	

Paleness of the surface	Bacteria	Acriflavine immersion
	Damage by cold	Heightened temperature
Paleness of the lens	Worm cataract	Avoid using worms from open waters!
	Fungus infection	

Body

Swollen belly	*Ichthyophonus*	
Protruding scales	Liver damage due to faulty diet	
Dropsy	Infectious bacteria	Destroy the fish

Nervous system and swim bladder

Erratic swimming	*Ichthyophonus*	
Shimmying motion, fish often on bottom (especially livebearers)	Chill	Even, high temperature

GLOSSARY

Acid water: water having a pH of less than 7·0; the lower the number, the greater the acidity (see also pH).

Acriflavine: a deep orange-colored powder, made up of a mixture of 2,8-diamino-10-methylacridinium chloride, 2,8-diaminoacridine, and chlorine, used a as bactericide.

Alkaline water: a pH of more than 7·0; the higher the number, the greater the alkalinity (see also pH).

Animalcules: infusoria.

Ammonia: NH_3.

Antibiotic: A substance produced by one kind of microorganism that is capable of inhibiting or killing other microorganisms.

Aureomycin: (also called chlortetracycline) an antibiotic of the formula $C_{22}H_{23}ClN_2O_8$ (7-chloro-4-dimethylamino-1,4,4a,5,5a,6,11,12a-octahydro-3,6,10,12, 12a-pentahydroxy-6-methyl-1,11-dioxo-2-napthacenecarboxamide).

Blood larvae: commonly called bloodworms, the aquatic larvae of the *Chironomus* midge.

Carbonate: a compound, CO_3, derived from carbonic acid.

Chloramine: a white or light yellow powder, $C_7H_7O_2NSClNa.3H_2O$, used as an antiseptic.

Chlorine: an element, usually in the form of a greenish yellow gas.

Chlorinated lime: a white or grayish powder made up of a mixture of Ca $(OCl)_2$, $CaCl_2$, $Ca(OH)_2$, and H_2O, with a maximum chlorine content of about 39%. Used in bleaching and in disinfecting water.

Copper sulphate: (also called cupric sulphate) a bluish powder, $CuSO_4$ (or $CuSO_4.5H_2O$), used as a dye, fungicide, bactericide, and emetic.

Flagellates: one-celled organisms with one or more whiplike hairs used for locomotion.

Gammarus: a freshwater shrimp.

Glass larvae: commonly called glass worms, the aquatic larvae of a gnat, *Chaoborus*.

Grindal worms: a small worm, believed closely related to the white worm.

Hard water: water containing a relatively high amount of dissolved calcium and magnesium; it is usually alkaline (see also Water Hardness).

Hypochlorous acid: an acid, HClO, formed by chlorine and water.

Infusoria: microscopic animal life.

Ion: an atom or combined group of atoms that have lost or gained electrons. As electrons are negative, the gain of an electron makes the ion negative (—), while the loss of an electron makes the ion more positive (+), as when water, whose formula is HOH (or H_2O) is split into H^+ and OH^-.

Malachite green: metallic green crystals, $C_{23}H_{25}ClN_2$, used as a dye and an antiseptic.

Metabolism: the total body processes of producing energy from food, and building and destroying body tissue.

Methylene blue: dark green crystals, $C_{16}H_{18}ClN_3.3H_2O$ (3,7-[dimethylamino] phenazathionium chloride), used as a stain and disinfectant.

Mycobacteria: a group of bacteria containing those forms that cause tuberculosis and leprosy.

Nitrate: a compound, NO_3, derived from nitric acid.

Nitrite: a compound, NO, derived from nitrous acid.

Peat: a brown or brownish black substance made up of mosses and other plants partially decomposed in water, without air and under pressure, and partly changed to carbon.

Peat moss: any moss from which peat may be derived, but almost always this term refers to *Sphagnum* moss.

Peat moss filtration: somewhat misnamed, as peat, rather than peat moss, is usually utilized as one of the filter substances. The peat gives off humic and other acids to the water passing through the filter.

Penicillin: any of a group of antibiotics basically derived from mutated molds of the genus *Penicillium*.

pH: a measurement of the concentration of hydrogen ions (H^+) or their equivalent weight in grams on a scale running from 0 to 14. Hydroxyl ions (OH^-) decrease in number as the hydrogen ions increase, and increase in number as the hydrogen ions decrease. Hydrogen ions contribute to the acidity of the water, hydroxyl ions contribute to the alkalinity. At pH 7·0, the concentration of hydrogen ions equals the concentration of hydroxyl ions, and the water is neutral. (See also acid water, alkaline water, ion.)

Potassium permanganate: dark purple or bronze-colored crystals, $KMnO_4$, used in industry and as an antiseptic.

Quinine hydrochloride: a substance, $C_{20}H_{24}N_2O_2HCl.2h_2O$, in the form of soft fine strands that is used as an antiseptic and other medicinal purposes.

Quinine sulphate: a substance, $(C_{20}H_{24}N_2O_2)_2.H_2SO_4.2H_2O$, in the form of short stiff rods, used as an antiseptic and other medicinal purposes.

Resorbtion: the dissolving and reabsorbing back into the body substances or structures previously formed by the body itself.

Sodium bisulfite: a white powder, $NaHSO_3$ (or sodium metabisulfite, $Na_2S_2O_5$), used as a bleach, disinfectant, and antiseptic.

Sodium hypochlorite: a compound, $NaClO.5H_2O$, used as a bleach (Clorox, etc.), disinfectant, and antiseptic.

Sodium thiosulphate: a colorless or white powder, $Na_2S_2O_3O.5H_2O$, used as the photographer's "hypo," as an antiseptic, as an antidote for cyanide poisoning, and to remove chlorine from solution.

Soft water: water low in calcium and magnesium; usually netural to acid (see also Water hardness).

Water hardness: a measurement of the concentration of calcium carbonate and magnesium in water. In America this is most often measured in parts per million (ppm), but in Germany it is measured in degrees of hardness (DH); one DH equals 18 ppm. Water containing from 216 to 324 ppm of calcium carbonate and magnesium is considered hard water; below 216 is medium-hard, above 324 ppm is very hard water. Water containing less than 144 ppm is considered soft.

INDEX